# a Gathering of Flowers

## A Book for Recording Birthdays
## & Other Special Occasions

THE CLEVELAND MUSEUM OF ART

Catalog No. A601
ISBN 0-7649-1633-5
Published by Pomegranate Communications, Inc.
Box 6099, Rohnert Park, California 94927, U.S.A.
(800) 227-1428; (707) 586-5500

Available in Canada from Canadian Manda Group,
One Atlantic Avenue #105, Toronto, Ontario M6K 3E7, Canada

Available in the U.K. and mainland Europe from Pomegranate Europe Ltd.
Fullbridge House, Fullbridge
Maldon, Essex CM9 4LE, England

Front cover image: *Florilegium,* p. 41: *Pansy and Violet* (detail)
French, 1608
Watercolor, ink, silver, and gold, over traces of graphite, on vellum, 31.1 x 20.2 cm
Gift of the American Foundation for the Maud E. and Warren H. Corning Botanical Collection,
1963.594

Cover designed by Lisa Reid

Printed in Korea

10 09 08 07 06 05 04 03 02 01   10 9 8 7 6 5 4 3 2 1

*Florilegium,* p. 42: *Carnations*
French, 1608
Watercolor, ink, silver, and gold, over traces of
graphite, on vellum, 31.1 x 20.2 cm
© The Cleveland Museum of Art
Gift of the American Foundation for the Maud E.
and Warren H. Corning Botanical Collection, 1963.594

1

2

3

4

January

8

9

10

11

12

13

14

15

16

17

18

19

January

20

21

22

January

26

27

28

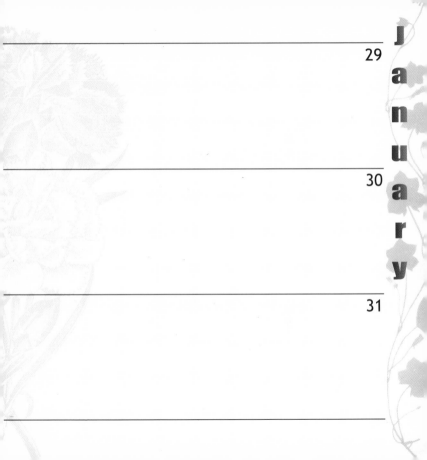

29

30

31

January

# February

## 1

*Florilegium*, p. 41: *Pansy and Violet*
French, 1608
Watercolor, ink, silver, and gold, over traces
of graphite, on vellum, 31.1 x 20.2 cm
© The Cleveland Museum of Art
Gift of the American Foundation for the Maud E.
and Warren H. Corning Botanical Collection, 1963.594

February

2

3

4

**February**

5

6

7

11

12

13

14

15

16

**February**

17

18

19

20

21

22

February

**February**

23

24

25

26

27

28/29

1

*Florilegium*, p. 32: *English Bluebells and Narcissus*
French, 1608
Watercolor, ink, silver, and gold, over traces of
graphite, on vellum, 31.1 x 20.2 cm
© The Cleveland Museum of Art
Gift of the American Foundation for the Maud E.
and Warren H. Corning Botanical Collection, 1963.594

2

3

4

5

6

7

8

9

10

11

12

13

14

15

16

17

18

19

23

24

25

26

27

28

March

29

30

31

*Florilegium*, p. 5: *Tulips*
French, 1608
Watercolor, ink, silver, and gold, over traces of
graphite, on vellum, 31.1 x 20.2 cm
© The Cleveland Museum of Art
Gift of the American Foundation for the Maud E.
and Warren H. Corning Botanical Collection, 1963.594

1

2

3

4

5

6

7

8

9

10

11

12

13

14

15

16

April

April

20

21

22

23

24

25

26

27

28

29

30

*Notes*

# May

1

*Florilegium,* p. 38: *Lily*
French, 1608
Watercolor, ink, silver, and gold, over traces of
graphite, on vellum, 31.1 x 20.2 cm
© The Cleveland Museum of Art
Gift of the American Foundation for the Maud E.
and Warren H. Corning Botanical Collection, 1963.594

2

3

4

May

5

6

7

May

8

9

10

11

12

13

14

15

16

May

17

18

19

23

24

25

29

30

31

1

*Florilegium,* p. 66: *Roses*
French, 1608
Watercolor, ink, silver, and gold, over traces of
graphite, on vellum, 31.1 x 20.2 cm
© The Cleveland Museum of Art
Gift of the American Foundation for the Maud E.
and Warren H. Corning Botanical Collection, 1963.594

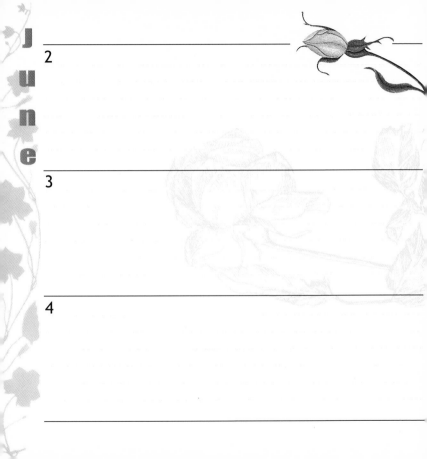

**June**

2

3

4

5

6

7

**June**

8

9

10

11

12

13

14

15

16

# June

**20**

**21**

**22**

23

24

25

26

27

28

29

30

*Notes*

1

*Florilegium,* p. 43: *Assorted Flowers with Snake*
French, 1608
Watercolor, ink, silver, and gold, over traces of
graphite, on vellum, 31.1 x 20.2 cm
© The Cleveland Museum of Art
Gift of the American Foundation for the Maud E.
and Warren H. Corning Botanical Collection, 1963.594

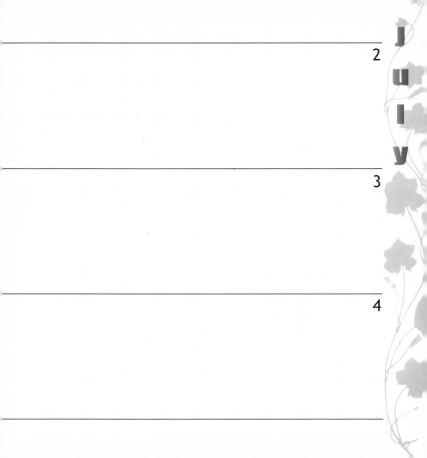

**J**
**u**
**l**
**y**

2

3

4

J
U
L
Y

5

6

7

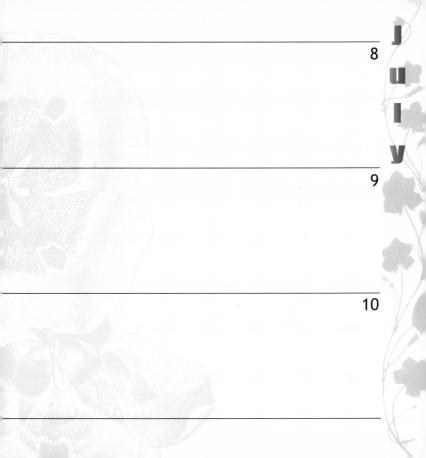

8

9

10

11

12

13

17

18

19

J
u
l
y

23

24

25

26

27

28

# July

**29**

**30**

**31**

1

*Florilegium,* p. 68: *Assorted Flowers with Moth*
French, 1608
Watercolor, ink, silver, and gold, over traces of
graphite, on vellum, 31.1 x 20.2 cm
© The Cleveland Museum of Art
Gift of the American Foundation for the Maud E.
and Warren H. Corning Botanical Collection, 1963.594

2

3

4

5

6

7

August

8

9

10

August

11

12

13

August

14

15

16

17

18

19

## August

**20**

**21**

**22**

23

24

25

# August

26

27

28

29

30

31

# September

1

*Florilegium,* p. 49: *Cornflowers*
French, 1608
Watercolor, ink, silver, and gold, over traces of
graphite, on vellum, 31.1 x 20.2 cm
© The Cleveland Museum of Art
Gift of the American Foundation for the Maud E.
and Warren H. Corning Botanical Collection, 1963.594

2

3

4

September

**September**

5

6

7

8

9

10

September

# September

11

12

13

14

15

16

**September**

17

18

19

20

21

22

# September

23

24

25

**September**

29

30

*Notes*

*Florilegium,* p. 16: *Tulips*
French, 1608
Watercolor, ink, silver, and gold, over traces of
graphite, on vellum, 31.1 x 20.2 cm
© The Cleveland Museum of Art
Gift of the American Foundation for the Maud E.
and Warren H. Corning Botanical Collection, 1963.594

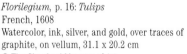

1

October

2

3

4

**October**

8

9

10

October

14

15

16

October

20

21

22

October

26

27

28

October

1

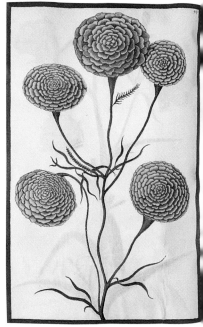

*Florilegium,* p. 54: *Chrysanthemum*
French, 1608
Watercolor, ink, silver, and gold, over traces of
graphite, on vellum, 31.1 x 20.2 cm
© The Cleveland Museum of Ar
Gift of the American Foundation for the Maud E.
and Warren H. Corning Botanical Collection, 1963.594

2

3

4

5

6

7

8

9

10

11

12

13

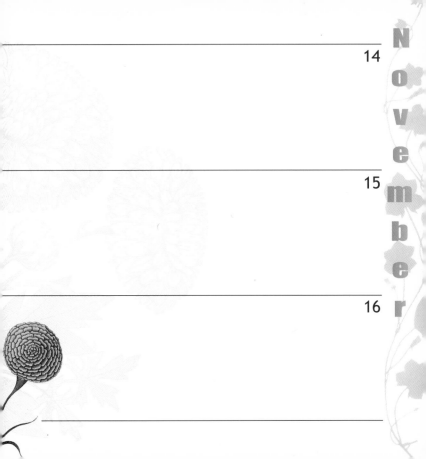

17

18

19

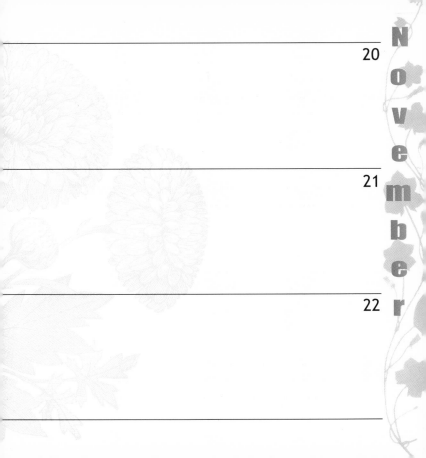

**November**

23

24

25

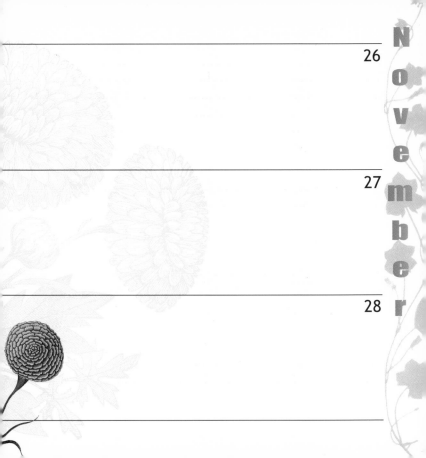

# November

**29**

**30**

*Notes*

*Florilegium,* p. 50: *Daffodil and Foxglove*
French, 1608
Watercolor, ink, silver, and gold, over traces of
graphite, on vellum, 31.1 x 20.2 cm
© The Cleveland Museum of Art
Gift of the American Foundation for the Maud E.
and Warren H. Corning Botanical Collection, 1963.594

1

# December

## 2

## 3

## 4

# December

8

9

10

# December

14

15

16

17

18

19

# December

20

21

22

24

25

# December

**26**

**27**

**28**

29

31

December

# Birth Flowers

| JANUARY | Carnation or Snowdrop |
| --- | --- |
| FEBRUARY | Violet or Primrose |
| MARCH | Jonquil or Daffodil |
| APRIL | Sweet Pea or Daisy |
| MAY | Lily of the Valley or Hawthorne |
| JUNE | Rose or Honeysuckle |
| JULY | Larkspur or Water Lily |
| AUGUST | Poppy or Gladiolus |
| SEPTEMBER | Aster or Morning Glory |
| OCTOBER | Calendula or Cosmos |
| NOVEMBER | Chrysanthemum |
| DECEMBER | Narcissus or Holly |

# Birthstones

| | TRADITIONAL | ALTERNATE |
| --- | --- | --- |
| JANUARY | Garnet | Rose quartz |
| FEBRUARY | Amethyst | Onyx |
| MARCH | Aquamarine | Jade |
| APRIL | Diamond | Carnelian |
| MAY | Emerald | Chrysoprase |
| JUNE | Pearl | Moonstone |

| JULY | Ruby | Carnelian |
| AUGUST | Peridot | Aventurine |
| SEPTEMBER | Sapphire | Lapis Lazuli |
| OCTOBER | Opal | Tourmaline |
| NOVEMBER | Topaz | Citrine |
| DECEMBER | Turquoise | Zircon |

## Zodiac Signs

| CAPRICORN | December 21–January 20 |
| AQUARIUS | January 21–February 18 |
| PISCES | February 19–March 20 |
| ARIES | March 21–April 20 |
| TAURUS | April 21–May 20 |
| GEMINI | May 21–June 21 |
| CANCER | June 22–July 22 |
| LEO | July 23–August 22 |
| VIRGO | August 23–September 22 |
| LIBRA | September 23–October 22 |
| SCORPIO | October 23–November 22 |
| SAGITTARIUS | November 22–December 20 |

| _Anniversary Gifts_ | TRADITIONAL | CONTEMPORARY |
|---|---|---|
| 1ST | Paper | Clocks |
| 2ND | Cotton | China |
| 3RD | Leather | Crystal or glass |
| 4TH | Silk or flowers | Electrical appliances |
| 5TH | Wooden items | Silverware |
| 6TH | Garnet or iron | Wooden items |
| 7TH | Wool or copper | Desk sets |
| 8TH | Bronze or pottery | Linens |
| 9TH | Topaz or pottery | Leather |
| 10TH | Tin or pewter | Diamond |
| 12TH | Linen or silk | Pearl |
| 15TH | Crystal | Watches |
| 20TH | China | Platinum |
| 25TH | Silver | Silver |
| 30TH | Pearl | Pearl |
| 35TH | Coral or jade | Coral or jade |
| 40TH | Ruby | Ruby |
| 45TH | Sapphire | Sapphire |
| 50TH | Gold | Gold |
| 55TH | Emerald | Emerald |
| 60TH | Diamond | Diamond |
| 75TH | Diamond | Diamond |